The Silent Owl

Illustrated by Sam McPhillips

Written by Clemency Pearce

Published by Top That! Publishing plc
Tide Mill Way, Woodbridge, Suffolk, IP12 1AP, UK
www.topthatpublishing.com
Illustration copyright © Sam McPhillips 2011
Text copyright © Clemency Pearce 2011
All rights reserved
0 2 4 6 8 9 7 5 3 1
Printed and bound in China

Creative Director – Simon Couchman
Editorial Director – Daniel Graham

Illustrated by Sam McPhillips
Written by Clemency Pearce

ISBN 978-1-84956-756-5

A catalogue record for this book is available from the British Library
Printed and bound in China

For Rob and Silkie - Sam
For Gemma, the noisiest bird I know - CP

In the great, old hollow oak,
Lived an owl, who never spoke.

Fox asked, 'Why do you never speak?'
But Owl refused to move his beak.

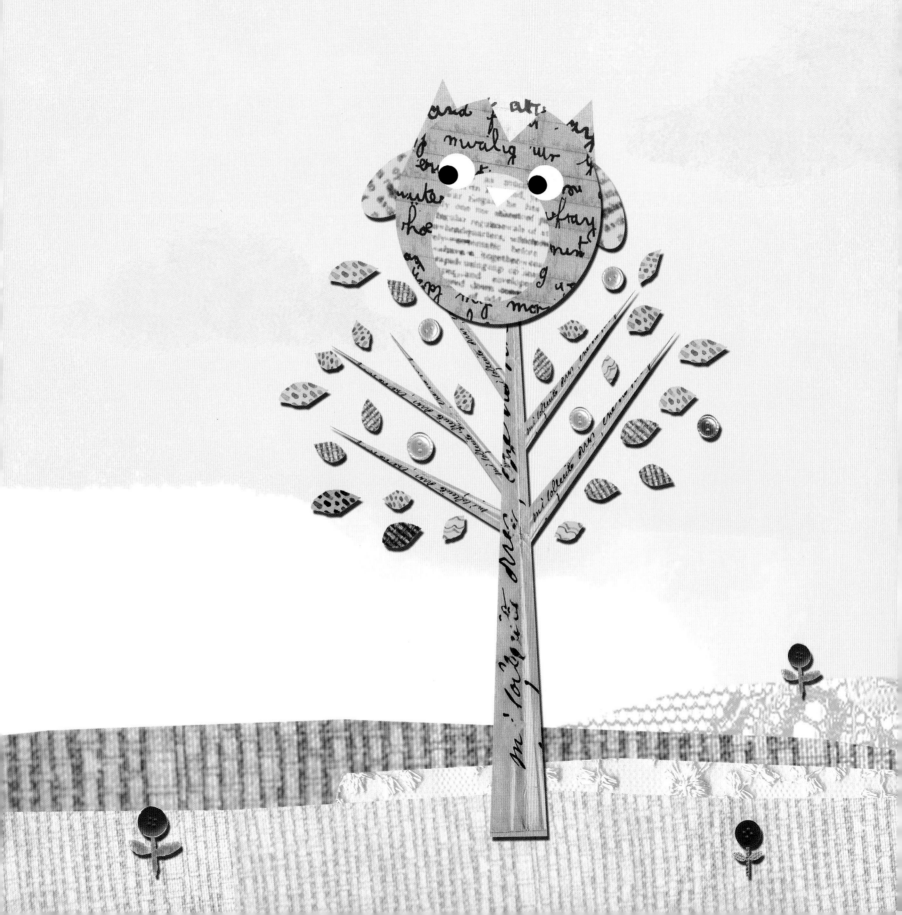

Badger huffed, 'How very rude!'
But Owl would not, could not, be moved!

A swooping bat whooped, 'Say hello!'

But Owl was silent far below.

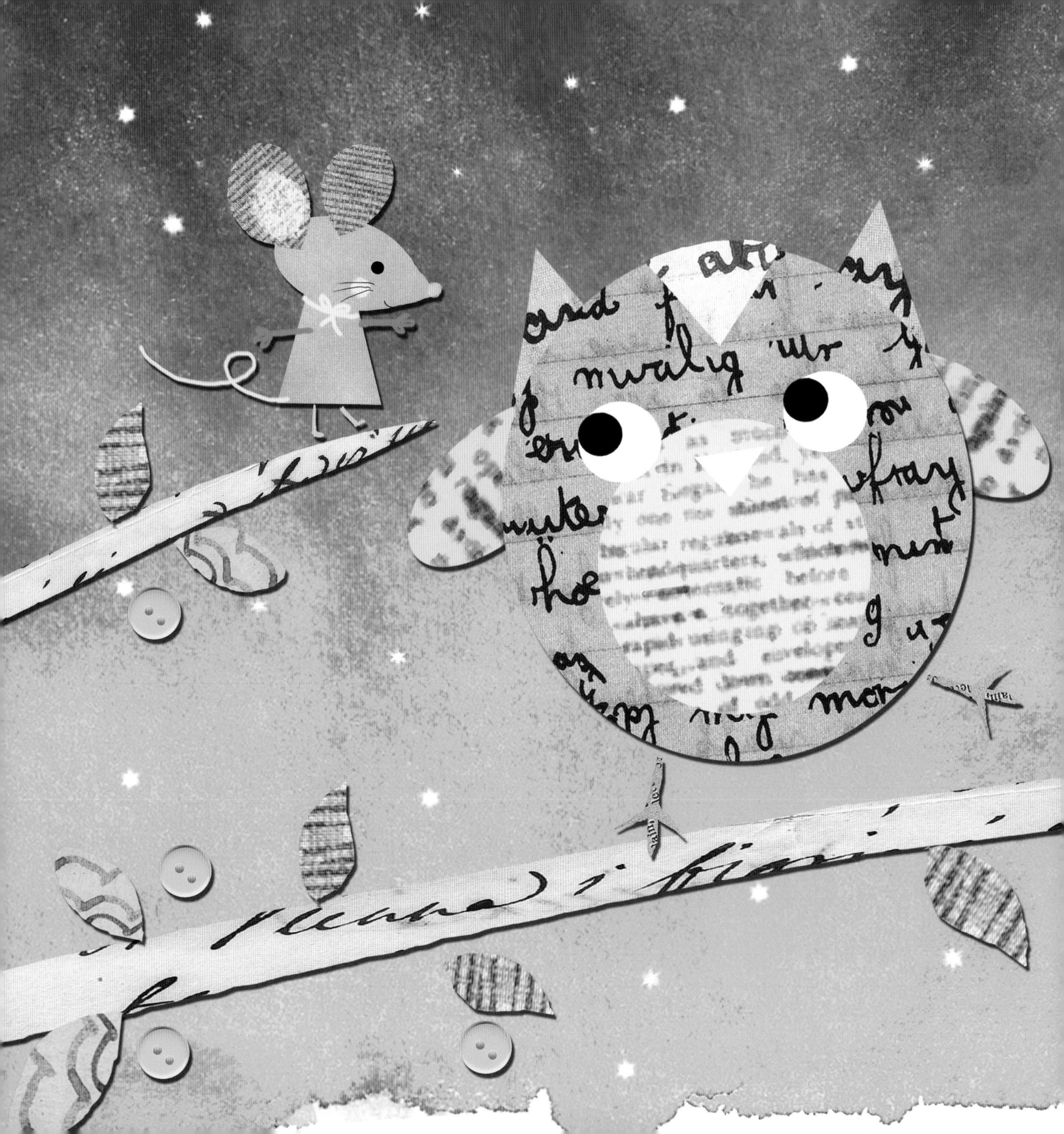

A pair of mice squeaked in his ear,
'Is it that you cannot hear?'
But Owl just rolled his giant eyes,
And stared up at the starry skies.

Squirrel scolded, 'Are you nuts?'
But Owl ignored his toothy tuts.

Rat cried, 'Owl! This isn't right!'
But Owl just gazed into the night.

Stag said, 'Owl! We need a sign,
To let us know that you are fine.'

So all the creatures gathered round,
To see if Owl would make a sound.

They stared at Owl; he stared right back.
Who would be the first to crack?

Stag declared, 'He must be mute,
Or he doesn't give a hoot!'

At this, the owl produced a trumpet,
A big bass drum and stick to thump it.

Although Owl wouldn't hoot,
he played the bongos,

piano,

guitar,

and flute!

The animals cheered, 'What a clever bird!'
And Owl just winked without a word.